FIRST STORY

First Story's vision is a society that encourages and supports young people from all backgrounds to practise creative writing for pleasure, self-expression and agency. We believe everyone has a unique voice, a story to tell and a right to be heard. Our flagship programme places inspiring professional writers into secondary schools, where they work intensively with students and teachers to develop young people's creativity, confidence and ability. Through our core provision and extended opportunities, including competitions and events, participants develop skills to thrive in education and beyond.

Find out more at firststory.org.uk

First Story is a registered charity number 1122939 and a private company limited by guarantee incorporated in England with number 06487410. First Story is a business name of First Story Limited.

First published 2022 by First Story Limited
44 Webber Street, Southbank, London, SE1 8QW

www.firststory.org.uk

ISBN 978-0-85748-501-4

1 3 5 7 9 10 8 6 4 2

A CIP catalogue record for this book is available from the British Library.

Printed and bound in the UK by Aquatint
Typeset by Avon DataSet Ltd
Copy-edited by Sophie Blacksell Jones
Proofread by Alison Key
Cover designed by Lee Harrison (http://leeharrison.daportfolio.com/)

A Key in the Incorrect Lock / Striding to the Write Place

An Anthology by the First Story Group
at Titus Salt School

EDITED BY ANDY CRAVEN-GRIFFITHS | 2022

FIRST STORY

As Patron of First Story I am delighted that it continues to foster and inspire the creativity and talent of young people in secondary schools serving low-income communities.

I firmly believe that nurturing a passion for reading and writing is vital to the health of our country. I am therefore greatly encouraged to know that young people in this school – and across the country – have been meeting each week throughout the year in order to write together.

I send my warmest congratulations to everybody who is published in this anthology.

Camilla

HRH The Duchess of Cornwall

Contents

Striding to the Write Place

Introduction

Andy Craven-Griffiths, Writer-in-Residence

The 2020–2021 academic year was unprecedented. The pandemic and lockdown were unexpected and understandably difficult. This anthology is like no other I've worked on in that respect. In other respects, it is very similar. There is still the variety of humour, sincerity, imagination and playfulness. There are still moments of brilliance I would have been proud of had I written them myself. The fact that we could still get in a room together, although remaining masked and in our specific areas, is testament to Francesca Skaife, Liz Chillington and Titus Salt School's Senior Leadership Team. Because of Covid, there were weeks when we had twenty pupils and others when we had only two. There were highly productive weeks and weeks that were a little more chaotic. I can only praise the staff and pupils both for making First Story happen and making it happen *in person* rather than online. It was a joy for me to be back in the classroom with both Year Seven and Year Ten pupils.

In the Year Ten group, we had Connor's humour and willingness to try something unfamiliar, Ruby's tenderness and pride in her poem about her mum, and the core trio of Eva, Ellie and Hannah producing high-quality writing each week. Without them, it would have been difficult to produce an anthology. They held the group together and brought more out of those around them. In Year Seven, we had a couple of standout sessions, including one on metaphorising emotions. We also had plenty of humour. There was consistently really strong writing from the likes of Sam and Isabelle, who were again a sort of stable core in a time of weekly flux. A special mention has to go to Ruby for her poem 'February 6th 2021'.

The poem is brave, vulnerable and emotionally honest, with brilliant flashes of simile and metaphor. I know it was difficult writing it. Often, that is the stuff most worth writing. When I read the poem back to Ruby, her face lit up – perhaps at having taken ownership of a difficult event, perhaps also at the quality of the writing, perhaps at something else. Either way, it was a special moment for me as a workshop facilitator. I will not forget it.

Teachers' Foreword

Francesca Skaife, Leader of English Transition, and Liz Chillington, Head of English Faculty

Resilters (*n. def.* resilient + writers = an accurate description for our First Story pupils during a difficult year)

At the end of our fifth year working with First Story, we have been impressed with the resilience and commitment of our pupils, despite a challenging year for us all. We were once again partnered with Writer-in-Residence Andy Craven-Griffiths, who worked tirelessly to help us re-engage our learners in creative writing. Our Year Seven and Year Ten pupils all responded positively to his enthusiastic nature, and all were inspired to improve their writing through his wealth of examples – perfectly chosen to highlight the skill he was modelling and evoke a wide range of emotions in them.

We would also like to thank First Story for supporting our school throughout the process; in particular, Andy Hill, the Regional Programme Manager, and Jay Bhadricha, the Editorial Content Manager. Your guidance, patience and understanding were greatly appreciated during the uncertain times we've experienced.

We are pleased to have had the opportunity to showcase both writers and illustrators again this year and to highlight the many talents our pupils have. Writers in both groups gladly accepted the opportunity to work with a professional writer and have shown both resilience and ambition throughout the sessions. The Year Ten pupils showed a real drive to improve their creative writing, with a clear focus on enabling themselves to produce the best narrative/descriptive task for their upcoming

GCSEs. They were very clear about their desire to learn the art of planning a solid story structure, using dialogue and using 'show not tell' techniques. After experiencing the limits of remote learning during the previous year, the group needed some time to adjust to the setting and warm up to sharing their ideas, but by the end of the programme, pupils' confidence had increased enough to engage with and support their peers and to discuss their editing and refining process.

The Year Seven group really appreciated the opportunity to just sit and think for a bit and to experience the sort of extra-curricular environment previously made impossible by the pandemic. Some of our Year Seven writers responded to this with real excitement, while others were more cautious, feeling their way around working in this different way, so it was sometimes a balancing act running the sessions. Out of this tension, though, there were moments of brilliant illumination, when the excitement was tamed onto the paper, or the more diffident found the right words.

Our illustrators this year gave up their own time after school to take part in the illustrating workshop, and we are so grateful to them for this. This year, as well as pencil, biro, ink and collage, they experimented with chalk and pens on black paper, and we think the end result has worked fantastically.

As always, running the project successfully has needed support from many people around school. We would like to thank all the staff who have supported us throughout the year, but particularly Jen Dewhirst for organising the illustrating workshop that allowed us to highlight our pupils' creative skills in a different way. We are also grateful to the Administration Team for their help and for the continued support from our Senior Leadership Team: we are pleased that they share our enthusiasm for being able to offer these opportunities to promote creativity within our school.

Thank you all for enabling us to continue to offer this opportunity.

A Key in the Incorrect Lock

Past, Present, Future

Year Seven

2020 was lockdown hell.
It was a prison the shape of your house,

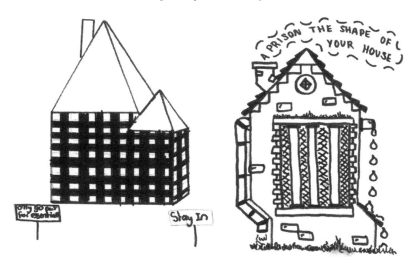

A darkening void and a hellish plague.
It was terrible broken trees.
It was the sad lips of a dog.
It was a black-and-white movie in a foreign language with
    no subtitles,
A robot that always breaks.
2020 was an English lesson where you learnt the same thing
Over and over and over again.
Sometimes it was a fluffy grey blanket,
Or a warm swimming pool,
Other times it was a bird pooping on the back of your neck.

2021 is a break from a nightmare,
A release from prison.

It is a snap of pressure,

The bang of a hammer.
It is people giddy from sugar.
2021 is the blasting part from the
    2020 firework.
It is the moment after having a
    tooth taken out at the dentist.
Sometimes it is a rotting corpse in an
    abandoned swamp.

At others it is like being in a storm at sea
and suddenly finding the calm at the centre.

2022 will be payback, the end of a war.
As strange as a dog walking backwards,
As unexciting as meeting your weird cousin.
It will feel as eventful as a year in Ibiza.
2022 will probably be like a fire burning its brightest,
Like the caramel inside a doughnut,
A new future for the next generation
Where you can meet your friend at the park without planning
    it first.
It will be like getting a strike in bowling
When last time you got a spare.

Surrealist Dictionary

Year Seven

Annoyance	A sticky, yellow sauce
Blood	Being scared of something
Chaos	A creature that lives in the ocean with eight tentacles
Clock	A natural event that happens to every living thing eventually
Death	An item that helps you to be on time
Dog	A feeling of happiness
Empathy	Something that you hold to help you to see
Fear	Something that keeps you alive
Feet	Something not human, like a monster or the undead
Grapes	The character trait of being strange and weird
Gratitude	The stuff on a flower that makes honey
Happiness	Something humans use to travel long distances through the sky
House	When everyone is calm, and no one is angry or upset
Inhumanity	The food that has been through your digestive system
Jealousy	Frozen water
Kindle	A way of understanding each other
Kindness	A useful object that helps people create straight lines

Lantern	The trait of being nice to another living thing
Laziness	A bone in your head
Madness	The part of your body connected to your leg
Mustard	Saying the opposite to what you mean in order to be funny
Nervousness	A thing you beat with wooden poles to get music out of it
Octopus	The bad feeling of wanting what someone else has got
Oddness	An ancient artefact, used for...
Peace	A planet full of life
Poo	When somebody is triggering you
Quiet	A pale person who drinks your blood like the juice of a cherry
Recklessness	A creature that has been domesticated over thousands of years but was originally used for hunting and protection against predators

Ruler	A person who doesn't want to do anything
Sarcasm	A thing that you put on your head to protect yourself
Skull	A natural disaster
Thought	A device that you can read on
Tree	When a person is crazy or insane
Ugliness	Being like a mouse and not saying a thing
Viciousness	An anxious, shrunken orange
Whale	A doll woman who rules the world and has shiny jewels
Xylophone	When nothing is troubling you
Youth	A sea creature that shoots bucketloads of water out of its back
Zipwire	The feeling you get when you look over the edge of a cliff

Optimist's Dictionary

Year Seven

Abomination	An experiment, a new hybrid between two species
Blood loss	A good way of falling asleep
Creation	A way to create life
Danger	A gentle reminder to be more careful
Exhaustion	The bus stop on the journey to good rest
Frog	A funny-noise-making, living toy
Grave	A permanent bed
Hiccups	A thing that makes you laugh when your friend gets it, and you don't
Inmate	A new friend you get to see every day
Jealousy	A meter for how much you love someone
Kangaroo	An amazingly cute animal with a built-in pocket for its phone
Life	Something that gives energy to turn stuff into movement
Mutant	Two times the legs, two times the food
Nitrous oxide	Something that freezes you in time so that you have more of it
Ocean	The playground of beautiful fish, dolphins and seahorses
Pain	A good present for someone you hate
Question	Something you are not sure about but love
Roundabout	A thing you find in a playground that is fun and joyful as it spins you around, gives you 360-degree vision and helps you to check no one is stabbing you in the back

Social anxiety	Something that makes social distancing very easy
Tree	A life-bringing provider of oxygen, cherries and conkers
Used	Pre-loved
Vet	A place you go to that prevents your pet from being in any more pain
Walking	A way of getting around that is good for the planet
X-ray	A way to help you not die by showing your bones
Yo-yo	A toy that goes up and down and makes you feel powerful because it does as it is told, and it always comes back to you
Zebra	A funny-looking, stripy, whimsical animal

Portmanteau Dictionary

Year Seven

Applease — When you give someone a Pink Lady and ask for forgiveness

Boxdinary — Someone who is nothing special at boxing

Camoflamingo — A flamingo in disguise

Daughterth — The female child of our planet

Elephantree — A huge tree with an enormous trunk

Fantasticky	A really good glue
Historead	A trip to the library to educate yourself on the past
Impasta	Somebody pretending to be an Italian cook
Justice-n't	When somebody follows all the rules and doesn't get what they deserve
Kangaroom	An enclosed space with a handy pocket
Locket-kat	A small ornamental case that is made from chocolate

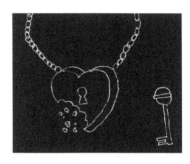

Mangoat	A scruffy, sheep lookalike that smells quite fruity
Numerator-nado	The top half of the violently rotating winds
Orangutangle	An orange, fuzzy monkey that gets in a muddle
Perisc-hope	Something that helps you see better things round corners

Qualiteens	The best 13- to 19-year-olds
Rememberet	A French hat that stops you forgetting

Suspisci-buzz	A noise that you do not recognise
Tangoat	An Argentinian dance you do with a shaggy-haired mammal
Un-dear	When you send a letter but you address the recipient sarcastically
Varietea	A person or place that is well stocked with herbal remedies
Windoughnut	Eating sugary treats to help you see things in perspective
Xylo-foam	A musical instrument made out of foam
Yesterdazed	When you are confused about the day before today
Zeb-bras	Items of underwear worn by black-and-white stripy animals

An Animal Called Panic

Sabeer Ahmed

Its black skin covers its small, jagged body.

Its jelly-like scales are like a safe and don't let anything in.

It pants quickly, and its sweat is like watching your teacher read your work.

You'll meet it when you are really worried about something happening, like getting an injection before going on holiday.

It lives in worried people's minds.

It moves around fast and makes sudden movements, like a sidewinder chasing a kangaroo rat.

To tame it, you must be calm, show no fear, move slowly, and act like you want to make friends with it.

A Key in the Incorrect Lock!

Sabeer Ahmed

I put a contact lens in my eye, like putting a key in the incorrect lock, and didn't know how to take it out. After a month my eye started hurting as though a pirate was cutting it open. My mum finally found out and took me to the hospital. It felt like when you get your brand-new football confiscated at school, and she takes you there to get it back. The doctor arranged two appointments. It was serious. In each appointment they scraped a needle on my eye, like glass, about twenty times. When the appointments ended, I got a huge cookie, like finally being rewarded after going through the pain. Just as I got the cookie, my sister took three big bites out of it. It was like scoring a goal in football but then the referee blowing the offside whistle.

A Creature Called Distrust

Eleanor Anness

Its see-through skin that addles the mind
Its rough skin like leather
Its breath like mouldy eggs
Its voice, a low broken hum that fills the room
It stares into my soul, hoping to find something good
It can be found in the murmured whispers of people talking
    behind your back
It will be met when the rumours are spread
It strides around the room looking for your deepest secrets.

Survival

Eleanor Anness

I wake up to the smell of chemicals. My mind tells me to run, to wake my sister up, shouting, 'It's a life-or-death issue!' Out of the corner of my eye, I see my dog charging for the door. Then I hear a bang. I grab as much as my bag can hold: a loaf of bread, a bottle of water, food for the dog and a silver necklace my mum gave me as a child. Then my sister mouths, 'Fill my bag up.' The second bang is much closer. 'We need to go now!' I command.

I think we have been running for ten minutes when I hear another bang. Then my mind tells me that I will now have to become the mother figure. A day later, I know that I have failed badly as supplies run short.

Later, as the sun sets, I catch a glimmer of civilisation in the distance. With renewed confidence, I say, 'Let's keep going.'

About two hours later, we make it to the town and find the news that shakes our universe. Everyone back home is dead. Still to this day we are unsettled about what has happened.

We reach a shop, and my sister stares at the luscious cakes; both our mouths water, but I know I will have to disappoint her again. It is against my inner feelings, but in order to survive in this big, new town, I will have to make a sacrifice. I realise my necklace may be worth enough to trade and help to see us through the next few days. I hand it over and witness the heartbreak on my sister's face as we give away the last bit of home we have in order to survive.

A Creature Called Excitement

Harry Armitage

Its colourful skin makes you feel joy at the touch.
Its fur is as soft as talc,
and it smells like chocolate cake.
It runs around like a crazy toddler.
It makes you laugh like a new-born baby,
and it's constantly trying to make you smile or laugh.
It has the ability to help you through the bad times.
It is happiness but better.
You can make friends with it if you catch it and stroke its back.

Sunse

Rose Beetham

Sunse is a beautiful golden griffin
who loves to make others happy,
but she has a bad history.

NEVER attempt to touch her without consent,
or she will poison you.

For Sunse to allow you to touch her,
you have to find a naturally grown apple
and feed it to her.

First Time Watching a Horror Movie

Isabelle Day

The five of us arrived at my friend's house like a bunch of mad
    hatters.
We ran up to our room like Usain Bolt in the Olympics.
After a lot of talking, we set up the beds, like maids.
Then got drinks galore.
The room was our cinema.
The film started with a disturbing image of tall grass
swaying in the wind like slim ballerinas.
This made me scared, as if I was being chased by stampeding
    bulls.
I clutched onto the closest pillow,
and didn't let go until it was over.
The scariest part was when
the male lead got his soul taken over by a demonic rock.
I hid behind the person closest to me.
After a while I fell sound asleep,
just as deep as Aurora the princess.
When the film came to an end,
I was abruptly awoken, thinking I was at war.

A Creature Called Anxiety

Libby Elliott

The green skin wrinkles to your touch.
He has horns and slithers like a fat snake mixed with a
    phoenix.
He stinks like a rotting corpse.
His breath smells even worse,
    like bird poo. Ew!
It wants you to feel panic and
    pressure so much that you
    forget EVERYTHING.
He lives in the dark corner of
    your room,
Drooling and staring as it waits
    to give you a panic attack.

It gets you really scared around people as it whispers, 'They're
    talking about you.'
He never sleeps.
His blood is like black tar.
He is basically immortal.
The eyes of anxiety are about as red as blood.
He likes to show up when you're going out, when you are
    going to the shops or maybe around strangers.
He does not like it when you are happy.
He does not like it when you're enjoying yourself.
When you're around other people, that's when he strikes.

A Creature Called Death

Sam Lines

I met it at the hospital.

It was wearing its father's skull as a helmet.
I stroked its black skin, but it hurt to touch.

I know that when the time comes it reveals itself to you.
If it deems you worthy, it will allow you to live.
But you must sacrifice others to stop it from sacrificing you.
If it doesn't deem you worthy, then it will devour your soul.

It grows larger with every soul it eats.
The larger it is, the stronger it is.
When I met it, it was only five foot tall, but it can grow to be
twenty foot.
When it reaches twenty foot, it will possess enough power to
end the world.
I knew a way to delay it.
I had to give it a sacrifice.
Other than humans, its favourite
food is goat.
I offered it a goat, and it gladly
accepted.

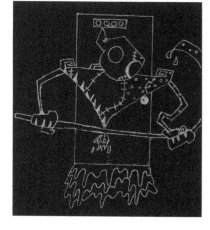

Speedboat

Sam Lines

My uncle pulls the cover off his speedboat as if he is unveiling the grand prize on a game show. Me, my mum, my aunt and my uncle jump on the boat, and he starts driving like he's Sonic. Within a few seconds, land is nowhere to be seen. He calls me over, sits me in the driver's seat and shows me how to drive it. I set the speed to max, and the boat starts going as fast as a cheetah. We hit a small wave, and the boat starts flying as if it's a bird. My mum and my aunt are at the back screaming as loud as rockets taking off. They are inches away from being engulfed by the blue abyss.

The Sacrifice

Sam Lines

I wake with a jolt. 'That was a crazy nightmare,' I think to myself. I get dressed and go downstairs. I see my dad pouring milk from the cereal box and cereal from the milk carton. He proceeds to get a fork out and hand it to me. I say nothing because he's been acting strangely ever since Mum died. I finish my breakfast and grab my bag.

'Bye Dad,' I shout.

'Bye Matt,' he shouts back.

I set off for school.

As I turn the corner, I see a dog. But this is no ordinary dog. This dog is standing on its hind legs holding a leash. Connected to that leash is a grown man on his hands and knees, wearing a collar. His name is Michael, I think. He does strange stuff all the time, but this is the weirdest yet.

'Are you okay?' I ask, but 'WOOF!' is the only reply I get.

I decide to keep on walking.

During the rest of the walk, I see a zoo full of people, an ambulance placing injured people around the city, a baby pushing its mother in a pram, dustbin men dumping litter all over the streets and ducks feeding people bread.

I'm almost at school, when I see Mr Griffiths. He looks like he's walking a dog, but when I look down, I can see he's walking his pet fish. Okay, this is weird. Everything seems to be happening the wrong way round.

'What on earth are you doing?' I shout at him.

'What do you mean?' he asks. 'I'm just taking my fish for a walk.'

'Fish can't breathe on land!' I shout back.

'Well, where are they supposed to breathe? The ocean?' he says sarcastically.

'Yes!' I shout furiously.

He walks away.

I get to school, and my first period is computer science. I go to press the 'on' button on the code I've been making, when I realise it's already on. The idea of this code was to make everyday tasks easier. Then it hits me. The tasks I've seen people do are backwards, yet this hasn't affected me. The nightmare was real. My code has been taken over by a dark force and inputted a virus.

I try to delete it, but it sends a sharp pain into my head, and I have a flashback to my nightmare. I remember that the only way to delete it is to sacrifice myself. I take one last look at the code I've been working on for the past few months and at the world around me. I click delete. Instantly, I collapse to the ground. I hear the panicked noises of the other children, and then it's dead silent. I can't keep my eyes open any longer.

Zuzu

Emilia Lofthouse

My hands are fuzzy, and I wake up next to my own body.
'Am I dead? No, I'm… I'm…'
I look in the mirror.
'I'm a dog!'

I am astonished, and I can't do anything.
'Help, help!' I shout, but all that comes out are barks.

I hear something behind me. I see my body moving. It gets
down on all fours and squints at the bony fingers in front of it.

We decide to try to start our day as normally as possible and
make our way to the top of the stairs. I realise we might have
a problem.

Betrayal

Bryan Norminton

One day, I was walking round an open field to get away from everyone. I heard a song that sounded familiar. I walked towards the sound, but I couldn't see where it was coming from. I looked around and saw a big rainbow monster. It looked like a lollipop had thrown up on it. I reached out to touch it, and it put its head on my hand. It felt like a turtle with rough skin. It smelled me. I think it was sniffing for weakness. It looked at me like it could understand me with its beady eyes. We sat down on the floor having a picnic, and it gave me all my favourite food and games – it seemed like a friend the way it acted.

Out of the blue, another beast came along. A dark blue colour, as if it had just seen someone die.

I walked away as the beasts started talking to each other. It seemed that the monster I was hanging with was hanging with me so that it could betray and hurt the blue beast even more. I called the blue beast 'Sadness' because of the way it looked, and I chose sadness because of the way I think it feels. I called the other one 'Betrayal' because of the way he treated Sadness.

Alien Contact

Bryan Norminton

When the aliens contacted me, I was in a deep doze in class. They told me that they would get rid of homework and change the school so it would be more fun for all the children, and that they would make the teachers do the homework. They said they wanted me to burn all homework so that kids would be on their side and rise up against the government, and they said if I didn't, they would torture me with raisin biscuits. We thought that the aliens were nice, with all the things they were doing for people, but little did we know, the worst was yet to come.

A Creature Called Madness

Ruby Robinson

Its skin changes colour, it's soft and large.
It is fluffy and looks like candy floss.
Its breath smells like the circus, the sweet smell of popcorn and
    strawberry Starbursts.
It sounds like a child after an overload of sugary food.

It's got a body of an unpredictable elephant with the horn
    of a rhino that is glittery and is all the colours of the
    rainbow.
It glances at me for a few seconds but gets distracted easily.
It lives at the beach where fun fairs and carnivals take place.
You will meet it by the upside-down ice-cream stand.

It gallops, skips, prances towards me.
It wants to play jump around with you.
Like a toddler, it chases you around,
even if you don't want it to.
If you want to make friends with it, you must play with it
and be funny and nice by telling it a funny joke and sharing a
    laugh with it.
If you want it as your own, you must give it ice cream.
And all those sugary foods like doughnuts and churros can
    tame it.

February 6th 2021

Ruby Robinson

The call came through to my dad
like a bomb being dropped on our front doorstep.
Dad said we had to get to the children's hospice
as quickly as possible.
I stood there like a deer in the headlights of his words.
When we got close,
I started looking at pictures of my brother on my phone,
his face a bright sun.
We stopped at a small Tesco's to get something to eat.
I got a pink doughnut with sprinkles.
At the hospice, me, my mum, my dad and my oldest brother
all sat around Joel as though we were magnets all drawn
    together.
Five minutes after we got there, he went,
like a puppy falling asleep.
It felt like a black hole just swallowed me up.
But the thing is, I know he is safe now.
He can run around, speak and eat.
That's how I imagine him now.

A Creature Called Sadness

Lily-Mae Simpkins

Its skin is blue and purple,
hard and cold.
Touch it, and it drops like a dead flower.
It wants you to be sad,
Like my sister's room, like a graveyard.
Tell it a dad joke,
and it just stares at you.

My Creature Called Hunger

Romano Virr

It is blood red.
It is that sharp pain sensation in your stomach.
It lives in the back of the fridge behind the mouldy cheese.
Its breath stinks like sour milk.
It sounds like a slow-motion earthquake.
It crawls like a new-born baby.
It desperately needs nutrition.
Its only weakness is having a full belly.

Striding to the Write Place

Ways to Guarantee a Better Future

Year Ten

Delete maths.
Keep on learning.
Don't be a murderer.
Don't lie to your mother.
Don't betray your friends.

Respect people around you.
Have more young politicians.
Teach different areas of history.
Be in the right place at the right time.
Make everybody learn sign language.

Don't get into trouble or commit a crime.
Kill everyone who is bad with a massive death ray.
Don't make the people on Wall Street so rich.
Pour water into your milk (to learn to be grateful).
Don't be greedy, and give to charity whenever you can.

If you see someone struggling, just help them, or just talk to them.
When using the school toilets, leave the door open (assert dominance).
Lead your person on a treasure hunt that ends in a love letter and a proposal
Give to charities as much as you can and raise money for the less fortunate
Make it mandatory to watch *Clarkson's Farm* (to learn how to farm).

Never forget your mum, even if you get rich and famous.
Take all Jeff Bezos's money and solve world issues.
Don't spend your life wishing you were older.
Partake in at least one dancing flash mob.
Compliment at least one person a day.

Always work hard for what you want.
Don't stare at your phone all day.
Fix global warming right now.
Have a teenage Principal.
Increase the minimum wage.

Get rid of Boris Johnson.
End the pandemic.
Go to school.
Eat the rich.
More art.

All These Brilliant Things

Year Ten

The first sip of water on a hot summer's day.
Late-night walks to clear your mind and get pineapple pizza.
Bubble wrap.
Cracking your knuckles.
Getting out of the car at services to stretch your legs.
Dancing in the rain.
Blasting good music.
Drinking water after exercise.
Watching your best friend realising she's wrong.
Listening to 'Space Oddity' by David Bowie when star-gazing.
Late-night calls with friends to laugh the day away.
Running your cold hands along the radiator after coming in
    from the rain.
When the McDonald's worker puts extra food in the box.

Mum's Favourite, Blueberry Pancakes

Ellie Collinge

'The chemo isn't working,' the doctor explained to my mum.

She tripped on the stairs this morning, so I went to help her off the bus after work. She stepped one foot off the bus and stumbled. I ran over to get her, and I sat her on the closest bench. I asked her if this had happened before, and she shook her head and said, 'I'm fine,' but she was staring at the floor when she said it. She stopped taking the chemo. She stopped taking everything. I told her she needed to keep going, but she told me that it was her body, and she would decide what she did with it.

They said she had six months left. I told her there and then that I was engaged to my boyfriend. He had asked me over a month ago, but I didn't want to mention it. I asked her to promise me that she would stay alive to see me at my wedding next year.

I booked tickets to Greece. Me and my dad were on the beach. My mum didn't come with us. My mum stayed at the hotel, lying in bed. When me and my dad left for the beach, she was sitting on the bathroom floor and resting her head on the toilet. She looked pale, and she was being sick all morning. But then the next day, we spent all day walking around the village in the blazing sun. Around the corner we saw an ice-cream shop, and me and my mum convinced my dad to get us one. She picked strawberry, and I picked mint choc chip. My dad didn't get one. He wasn't talking much that day, and he was constantly checking his phone. He would stay behind me and my mum when we were walking, and I would look back, and he would be pretending that he was not looking at my mum.

She decided she wanted to be at home near the end. Yesterday, I made her breakfast and lunch. When I went to collect her plates, there was still a sandwich with only one bite taken out of it, and the pancakes from breakfast had gone cold and were soggy. She didn't wake up until three o'clock.

This morning, trying to get myself out of bed was like trying to persuade a toddler to eat vegetables. The duvet, a big rock on top of me. Once I was up, I went to the shops to get some blueberries, started to make my mum's favourite blueberry pancakes. I got all the way into her room before I remembered. Her bed was made. It was empty.

Seven Ways to Ruin a Relationship

Ellie Collinge

Turn up to a first date over thirty minutes late.
Give no prior warning and no apology.

Tell your girlfriend you are going for a run every day.
Then leave wearing flip-flops.

Call them Molly when their name is Emily.

Start a series on Netflix without them.
Then lie about it.

Leave the milk on the side.
Claim it wasn't you.

Try to convince your partner to eat healthy,
me having a salad with celery whilst they are eating a burger.

Sit there nodding as if you are listening to them,
when really you are listening to the football in your
    headphones.

Am I Invisible?

Ellie Collinge

My arm was aching it had been up so long. I just wanted to answer Mr Roberts' question, but he asked Lauren, and she wasn't even looking. He asked again, and my hand shot right up. I shouted, 'Sir! Sir! Pick me! I know the answer,' but Charlie said, 'Shhhhhh,' so I put my hand down.

The boy on the front row threw an aeroplane across the room, and the teacher shouted, 'Pick that up now,' so I decided I would throw one too. The teacher looked directly at me. I thought he was going to shout at me, but then he continued to look further into the distance and, after what felt like ages, he shouted, 'Billy!' so I turned around to see who it was. It was a short blonde boy with glasses. He looked terrified. Why didn't he shout at me? It was obvious that I threw it.

Even though today was like every other day – nothing was different, people still ignored me – I had just had enough of it. After school I went to debate club. I stuck my hand up to give my opinion, and the teacher said, 'Yeah,' so I started to talk, but the other students started talking over me, and the teacher could not hear me, and I later realised she wasn't talking to me anyway.

At home I tried to ask my mum what we were having for tea, but she just started a conversation with my dad.

Later that night after a long day at school, I just closed my eyes for a moment. I saw someone who looked like me but wasn't me: they were taller and older. I was a bit confused that the more I looked at this person, the more she started to look like me. I watched her get on a train to work. She met a friend on the train, and she waved at some friendly faces on the street.

She looked happy. She went to lunch with her friends, and people actually spoke to her and paid attention when she was talking.

Then my eyes opened, and I realised that I was not actually the person I saw in my dream. It felt like I had lost something that felt good: the woman in my dream was all I have ever wanted; I just didn't know how to get it. She was noticed and appreciated. The dream felt like ages, but it was only thirty minutes. Maybe this is how I would finally be noticed, if I am an adult.

Later that evening I went to sleep wishing that in the morning I would wake up and finally get what I wanted and feel how I wanted.

I open my eyes, but I don't feel any different, so I get up and walk over to my mirror. I look, and I am taller, and I am older. I am an adult.

Maybe this will solve all my problems.

The Wildfire in My House

Ruby-Rose Crosdale

My Mum is a hot head.
My mardy attitude is probably the reason but my 'face like
     thunder' isn't always what you think it is.
My Mum is a smile in a morning and the smile at night which
     is the guarantee of calm after a stressful day.
My Mum is the lioness lurking in her lair,
Keeping the cotton wool and
     bubble wrap at the ready.
My Mum is a thousand kisses.
I remember that time when I
     toddled from Baildon to
     Shipley as though I was Bear
     Grylls, leaving Hannah on
     the bed as a newborn,
My Mum's initial instinct was to hug
     me like a slo-mo movie scene.
My Mum is the hulk of the home
     when she's left to do the

     housework without any help (Dad pull your finger out,
     none of us gets away with it).
My Mum is a wildfire.
My messy room is the Mentos to her Coke.
My Mum is that cosy-wosy feeling on a cold winter's day,
     pulling the clean, warm pyjamas from the dryer after we
     had fun sledging with Dad.
My Mum is the glue that holds everyone together.

History of Isabelle's Life

Kaitlyn Deakin

Isabelle was visiting her grandfather. She went up to her grandfather's library. As she was looking through the dusty, old books for something interesting to read, she found something like a family secret. She read the title of the book: *The Secret of Isabelle's Journey*. She began to read it. It was all about her family's legacy and how her family tree began.

Isabelle had many questions. She went down the long staircase that led to her grandfather's room, where he was always working on something important. As she was about to knock, he opened the door. It was time for dinner. When he saw Isabelle, he asked in a worried tone, 'What's wrong Isabelle?'

She seemed scared. Since Isabelle couldn't speak, she just lifted the book up. Her grandad just smiled and said to her, 'It's time for you to know about your legacy, Isabelle.'

Isabelle just looked at him in confusion and questioned, 'What legacy?'

'Come. Let's go eat, and after dinner I'll tell you all about it in my study. Is that okay?'

After her grandmother, her grandfather and her two cousins had finished their pizza, chips and salad, and then ice-cream for dessert, Isabelle and her grandfather went back upstairs to talk about their family history.

Her grandfather asked, 'Have you ever wondered about that birthmark on your shoulder?'

Isabelle looked at him and asked, 'Yeah I have. Why do I have this birthmark but nobody else in our family does?'

Her grandfather just told her, 'You are the only one that has that birthmark and it represents the night you were born and how strong you can be.'

Isabelle looked at him, shocked, and then at the birthmark on her shoulder. A crescent moon with a star, representing the night she was born.

Isabelle learned that her ancestors had lived in France back in the 1700s and that the first female had the name 'Isabelle'. This was how Isabelle got her name as the first-born girl of her generation. But when they were living in France, her family got attacked, so they built a vault with enough supplies, clothes, water and food to survive, plus their parents' belongings, so that they had something of theirs. When they knew that their village wasn't getting attacked anymore, they left all their things, packed up, hid the vault and decided to leave France. 'Isabelle' and her three younger brothers moved to Spain, where they lived in peace for nearly forty years. Just as they were building families of their own, they were attacked again, so they moved to England, where her grandparents met each other. They got married three years after they met and had five sons and two daughters.

Isabelle's grandfather continued that now she was of a certain age, she would have to go to France with her cousins to collect something that belonged to her family. For her to complete this mission, she would have to follow the clues that were left behind by her ancestor 'Isabelle'. She would need a map to help her find four different-coloured diamonds. She would also need to collect a certain necklace. Her grandfather told her that now that she knew what she needed to do, she would have to start training for the dangers that might come her way.

She walked down the staircase and saw her cousins. She asked them if they were also involved in this, and they just nodded at her and said, 'Welcome to the team, Isabelle!'

While Isabelle and her cousins were training, they were interrupted by Isabelle's parents arriving to pick her up and take her home. During the car ride she was quiet. She was thinking. She looked out of the window as if she had just seen a ghost, thinking about what she had just learned and what she must do.

Run, Rabbit, Run

Hannah Goulden

I've had enough of this. Every damn night this happens. Muffled screeching. I wonder if they enjoy it.

I know I wouldn't. It's incredibly selfish. I know I'll enjoy eating them when the time comes. I've always enjoyed rabbit. Sometimes I cover my ears, but when that doesn't work, I draw. I try to draw how the screeching makes me feel. A black void, with a feeling of being pulled down. Sometimes I'll draw what I want to do to the rabbits. Shout at them, comfort them, kill them. It can be a long time before Father goes and quietens them. Their voices sound broken and raspy, like they've been screaming for a long time. Then there is silence, and he comes into the room where I'm pretending to sleep.

'It's alright now darling, they won't disturb you again.'

'Thank you, Father.'

It's reached morning now. I rise gently, taking my time. I can't get up too quickly or else I'll hurt my back – it's been crooked ever since I was a child. I make my way over to the dress I usually wear. A beaten, bloody and worn dress. The one thing that I can call my own. Walking carefully, I make my way downstairs. Food already set on the table. Mother by the stove cleaning up her chopping board. Red oozing into the sink. Sitting down on the uncomfortable chair, I tuck into the meal. It tastes the same as it always does: chewy and weird. I don't like it, but I wouldn't dare tell them that. The last time I complained I was called ungrateful and wasn't allowed to eat for a week.

Father comes barging through the door, large bag on his back, hiding his hands in his pockets. He ignores us both, drops his bag on the floor, grabs his bowl, takes a large bite and sighs contently.

'One day they'll accept this.'

Before I can ask what, there is a loud smash outside, then more screeching. Father drops his bowl, shouting out a very loud and rude word. He grabs his rifle and runs outside, leaving a large mess of stew on the floor and his bag, open, the contents spewing out on the floor. The buckle has been broken for as long as I can remember. I expected the handgun, the ammunition. But I'm sure you don't need handcuffs and gags for rabbits.

Things that are Incredibly Concerning

Hannah Goulden

1. When people eat KFC with a knife and fork.
2. When people say that the new presenters of *Top Gear* are better than the first.
3. Saying that the *Star Wars* sequel trilogy is amazing.
4. When people shake hands for over three seconds.
5. Not liking David Bowie.
6. Not listening to old but gold music.
7. Eli Roth movies.
8. Boris Johnson.

Spirits

Eva Murray

I saw the life drain from them. I felt their presence vanish, but all I could do was sit and watch. I had no control, but neither did they.

I still remember the smell on their breath, a stomach-curdling smell. It washes over me sometimes and leaves me in a sort of cold shock, my body paralysed, my face blank of emotion, but my mind racing with the feelings attached to the memories that flash before me.

I remember the first time they began to disappear; it was on my fourth birthday. Even though I didn't like it, I understood: they were stressed, and it was tempting. I miss them, the old them, the warm them, the kind them.

Except that person left me when they lost themself. It happened slowly at first, and then caught up quick; out of nowhere, they went, dragged, drowning, but of their free will.

I don't want to be like them, yet, reflected in your eyes, I know I'm starting to go too often too.

The Lord of Light

Ben Reed

Light, the first thing those dark eyes have seen in a long time. I would feel bad for him… if I knew what he was. My eyes themselves could only see the void-like silhouette of the monster in front of me. To start with, it had horns as big as tusks protruding out of its head. But what struck me as most unusual was the bulk of this mighty being: apex levels of sheer muscle and in a humanoid form but beyond human. It strode towards me as if eager to rip my majestic torso in half.

I ordered him to 'Stop'.

He obeyed, so I asked him, 'What is your religion?'

He didn't respond, so I questioned him again.

His eyes came to colour; they flared as if an intense storm was trapped behind those pupils, a storm of fire, ash and ruin. They stared intensely into my soul, ripping out any pity I had maybe felt before. Eager to stretch my fingers, I got ready to draw my sword, as I had been instructed to do in a case like this.

'Who is your allegiance to? What is your religion?' I yelled into his face, questioning his motives and nerve as I persisted.

He raised his head and with a deep raspy tone responded with something even my superior was confused by. 'My only care is of the light. I have no need of anything else.'

Bewildered, I asked another question: 'What do you mean?'

In a muffled tone it replied, 'What you'd expect.'

Still in a state of confusion, I said, 'What would I expect? The one who made the light?' to which he shook his head. He was not a people person. This was clear from the frustratingly indirect answers I got from him.

He moved, looking ready to rip me in half if I tried to get in his way.

'You can't go that way,' I yelled to his rough, fur-covered silhouette, as he turned and stared at me. 'It is only for those worthy of heaven.' I drew my sword and ignited the flames of hell around it.

He did not flinch. I watched the bulky frame, the war-torn cracked horns, the hooves like an animal, but most importantly the eyes. Black, void of depth and meaning. He was a minotaur.

Nothing made sense. Nothing added up, and nothing was righteous about this scenario. Why would God not tell me that he intended to let a machine of war into paradise?

'You're a monster,' I whimpered in a low, shaky voice.

'Who are you?' he questioned and then continued, 'I've seen the endless halls of a glorified tomb for all my life. The labyrinth's empty corridors and lies cloud my mind eternally in a cycle of infinite torture. Men and halfwits come to die by my hand in a worthless attempt to prove themselves, and all they do is scar my mind with the thoughts of their endless deaths.'

'I'm Azrael, servant of God and Archangel of the four,' I replied, 'Why d'you let him kill you?'

'Because I knew there was something more than this,' he said with a heavy breath and a subtle anger. 'And to escape,' he said in a calmer voice than before. He'd spoken his mind and confessed his struggles. We were finally talking in sentences and getting along fairly well from what I could tell.

Finally, I made my decision. I opened the pearly gates and released the light he had craved for so very long now. He strode through with a solid intention, one that could even block out the bright orb he'd been searching for all these years, the entity of light. He stood staring at it for a full two minutes before turning around. Our gazes met. I looked into his eyes to see freedom shining and the void being infiltrated. Instead of black I saw a bright glare. That bright orb as bright and passionate as his will for freedom. The sun.

The Bridge

Josh Shackleton

The bridge went on for miles, stretching to the horizon.

Looking down to the forest floor made me dizzy. The bridge stretched above the treetops in the sky, the wood rotting and with holes in the planks, the rope blistered, and the moss glistened from the glowing sun.

Every step was painful. The darkness still followed closely behind, a fragment of emotion and stress that I was trying to run away from, but it was getting closer. I picked up the pace. Sweat beads dripped off my chin. The bridge moaned under my weight.

The emerald forest stretched down to hell and up to the heavens, and giant mountains loomed in the distance. Black dots moved around in the sky, circling one tree that was bigger than the rest. They were birds, but they looked too big. I kept walking, but I didn't get anywhere. I looked behind me.

All of a sudden, everything went dark.

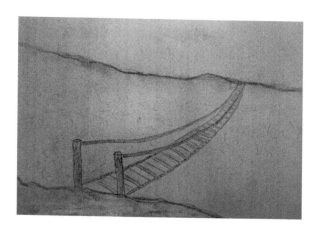

I woke up on another bridge, vision blurry, the air damp and cold, the wind sharp and painful. I stood up warily, using the ropes for support; they felt wet and yet were not. My vision cleared enough to get a look at the new scenery. The emerald forest and the mountains were gone.

All that was left were dozens of shrivelled-up trees covered in a cold, sharp and icy substance.

IT'S SNOW! I realised why the bridge was more slippery and wet than the last one and why it was so cold. My vision was now blurry because of the newly formed blizzard. I put my arm up to my face to shield my eyes, my ears stinging. My dark brown hair was now covered in snow. I'd been walking for what felt like a couple hours. My legs were getting weak, and my muscles were freezing up. My knees were red raw from falling on the icy bridge, which was disappearing in the snow.

Then my legs gave way, and my fingers wouldn't move. I grew faint. My eyes closed, and I fell.

I woke up. A warm gust of wind passed by my face, waking up my senses. I was on another bridge. My eyes now open, I stood up and turned to the source of wind to see a flock of baby birds with the mother in the lead. Below the birds were trees, all blooming pink and green through the melting snow. They were blossom trees and there was a variety of fruit trees dotted around.

I looked back. The darkness, the lingering fear was still chasing me, devouring everything in its path.

I looked ahead…

I saw a bright hole with a dark centre…

Only one thought came to mind. Is this the end?

My legs started moving, picking up speed, running,

FASTER, FASTER, FASTER, FASTER AND FASTER…

I came to a sudden stop at the end of the bridge.

I looked around and took a breath and jumped…

I woke up. Sweat running down my face and onto my bed sheets. The only light was from under the door. I could hear two people yelling and shouting at each other: my parents. I didn't want to go back to sleep, so I went to get a drink.

I looked back and the darkness wasn't following me anymore.

Top Five Minutes of My Life

Milly Starkey

1. Sending that break-up message after hesitating for hours.
2. The last lesson of PE in lockdown school, when we all banded together to play a big game of dodgeball (my favourite sport). My team won, but that isn't why the moment has made this list.
3. Feeling accomplished after doing the bungee jump in Switzerland.
4. Meeting my new group of friends from lockdown school for the first time in the summer and sharing a big tub of Crunchie ice-cream together.
5. Feeling accomplished after learning 'Hallelujah' – the very first song I learned to play on my ukulele – when I'd finally learned the right chords.

My Story

Milly Starkey

This had now been happening all my life, ever since my father died. But now more prominently than ever. Memories reshaping themselves as they see fit. Remoulding and merging into one. Fragments of other people's reality were disappearing from mine. Days were ending as fast as they were beginning, and my thoughts became meaningless. Usually, I'd count it as bad luck, but seventeen and a half years of bad luck may be a little too textbook for a student to be facing. It made no sense why I was this way, or what had caused it, but all I can remember from childhood was constant misfortune and suffering. It had just got worse, until eventually it had become normal and routine.

I wondered for hours at a time, day after day, why I was this way. The unbearable weight of others' opinions crushing me. People said I was different. I *was* different. I felt I didn't belong. Constantly being cast aside, I was treated as inhuman. It was unfair. Acceptance was my one wish, and yet it seemed so unreal, so far away and unreachable, constantly slipping through the net of my fingers when I needed to catch it the most. This was when it began. Or I guess you could say where it ended. I'd developed a need to be alone. Being by myself, alone with my thoughts and my interests. Away from anyone who tried to tell me different.

I fell asleep on a warm Tuesday night. It was a normal evening, as far as normal goes for me, I guess. I woke up as usual and headed to school. As I approached the gates, my vision became clouded, a tsunami of black fog flooding my eyes, and then it was gone, sprinting out of my body as fast as it had rushed in. It had confused me. But not in the usual way.

My day went on. I sauntered down the halls, which appeared to be empty. This was an unnatural sense; I developed an uneasy gut feeling that I couldn't seem to shake. My journey to the classroom continued, though now I was monitoring my every move. I'd never felt this way before. I took my seat. The feeling still lingered in my throat, almost making me ill, the sickening chill of neglect strangling me. By now, my classmates' voices and faces were merging into one as I sat on the stool. The hum of the speaker echoed around my skull. It bounced off every surface on the inside of my head, rattling around my brain. The sensation was unusual.

I stumbled to the bathroom, my ears now roaring with the ear-piercing shriek of booming rejection. I stared back at myself in the clouded mirror. Now, more than ever, I felt like I was different. I didn't look myself. I'd changed. Then silence. It was a cold silence. The type that would only occur on a winter's evening, or maybe even at a funeral. A frosty chill fluttered in the air, its wings brushing my nose.

There was a sudden presence in the room that wasn't there before. An unwanted presence. A shadow in the corner of my mind with the whisper of the deceased. I pushed it away. It kept calling, calling my name. The beckoning call of death serenading me. The temptation was murderous; it was roping me in, grabbing me by the throat and dragging me down its chilling path. I kept fighting it. All my strength went into that battle, but I was weak, weak-minded and weak-bodied. I've always known this.

What felt like an endless battle soon ended, the result not in my favour. Emptiness. Darkness. Silence. The shadow now leaving my head, circling me, now dragging me as it had done before, but this time knowing it had won. I didn't know what was to become of me. For now, my fate lay with Death himself. Though the most painful part of death was knowing I'd been beaten. This was what I'd tried so hard to prevent, though all my efforts had failed. Failed simply because I'd got what I'd always wanted. My past lust for a life of being solitary had finally caught up with me, and it was now at the point of no return.

Mafia

Harrison Turner

Winning had always been easy before. The family business had been strong for over seventy years! But today, the boss gathers us all up like a herd of sheep. He looks like a corpse. Usually, he's as fierce as a raging bull, but now he's as cold and pale as a ghost.

Trembling, he says, 'Th-th-thhe business…' hyperventilating. He seems like a panicking fly trapped in a foggy warehouse. He's drowning in sweat. 'So fellas, our ship has been sunk…'

Everyone scratches their heads.

'We have been too soft. We have listened to the government and stayed low. We all want to live the high life, but higher officials keep bribing us to keep the crime low, making it harder for money to come in!'

One week later

Frontline news: 'Mafia organisation run down and raided by Federal Bureau of Investigation.'

Top Ten Things You Can Fit in Your Pocket

Harrison Turner

1. Your feelings
2. A footlong for a good ol' scran on the go
3. A phone
4. A wallet
5. A crowbar
6. A severed hand
7. A soggy Tesco meal deal
8. Some socks I got ID'd for
9. A brand new multitool
10. A DL12YET6948KJU Toshiba washing machine

The Unexpected

Waliyah Waheed

One day last summer, the sun poured through my window. The morning chorus of the melodious birdsong aimlessly wandered through my room as I awoke from my sleep. I jumped out of bed and got changed. Just then a sweet smell filled my room. I rushed downstairs, and there I was welcomed with a stack of pancakes drizzled with syrup, scones filled with clotted cream and jam, and a luscious cup of hot chocolate calling my name.

As I looked around in confusion, I saw my dad wearing baggy blue overalls and holding two fishing rods in his right hand and in his other hand, a net and bucket.

'Did you forget what today is? Hurry up and eat. I want us to get there as soon as we can!' exclaimed my dad.

How could I forget we were going fishing? It's always the same day every year, but for some reason I always forget.

After eating my breakfast, me and my dad went to our favourite fishing spot. We left the house at the crack of dawn. After five minutes of searching for our perfect spot, we found it. My dad lowered the anchor, and I cast my fishing rod into the water. After half an hour of rotten luck, we decided to go further into the mysterious sea.

Once again, my dad lowered the anchor, and I cast my rod into the water. Surprisingly, after two attempts, I felt a large tug on my rod. 'Get the net ready!' I exclaimed. I reeled the unexpectedly heavy item I had caught. As it rose from the water, I realised I hadn't caught a fish or a random boot, I'd caught a metal box. I grabbed it out of the net and put it on my lap. Fixated on the box, I opened it. My dad's jaw dropped, and he began to sweat.

We rushed home. During the journey, my mouth was sealed shut. After what felt like days, we reached home. Immediately, my dad called the police. A few minutes later, there was a harsh knock on the door.

'I'm Detective Appleton and this is scientist Jemma Simmons. We got a call about an unexpected find on a fishing trip,' declared the man.

'Yes, that's right,' my dad replied.

'We would like to take a look, if that's okay?' said the detective again.

'Yes, that's fine. Follow me,' replied my dad.

'That's an unexpected find. We would like to take it to the lab and do a few tests. We'll get back to you in a week,' announced the detective.

'Thanks, detective,' my dad said.

Two weeks went by, and all I could think about was the treasure we had found. A few hours later, there was a knock on the door. I rushed down the stairs and flung the door open. It was the postman. The next day there was another knock on the door. 'FINALLY!' I thought to myself, 'The detective has come back.'

'Sorry I came late, but I've got some news.' He paused and smiled. 'The item you found was the bone of an elephant bird.'

'A what?' I said.

'An elephant bird. It's an extinct bird. They have been extinct for 100,000 years, and this was the first ever bone seen from this species. This is an extraordinary discovery, and that bone is extremely rare, so we would like to give you a £100,000 reward for finding it.'

* * *

Ten years passed by, and I was just about to show the world my biggest achievement. 'Can I welcome to the stage scientist Isabelle Jane,' the host of the show said. I stood up and made my way to the stage, while repeatedly praying I wasn't going to trip or embarrass myself. After all, I was about to speak in front of the Queen. I started by telling the story of how I ended up in the place I was today – the chief scientific expert on the elephant bird.

When I finished my speech, I went home and prepared for my fishing trip.

Stay Positive

Waliyah Waheed

When life is hard, and everything goes wrong
When you feel out of place like you don't belong
Focus on the positives, and you'll feel motivated
You will do better, when you follow the path God created
Set ablaze your negativity
Box and bury their insensitivity

Build your inner empire
Show them how you continue to build higher
There are opportunities at every turn
Choose wisely: love, laugh and learn.

Darren Pickford

Connor Wilson

His name's Darren Pickford. He's the stereotypical neighbourhood man: middle-aged guy, always smiling, starting to get grey hair but still wanting to try and help people with problems around the neighbourhood wherever possible. He goes to Aldi when his bank balance allows it, coming home with Aldi special buys: long-life milk, chocolate spread (the kids' favourite) and a loaf of bread to keep the birds fed. Home to the flat where the lock system doesn't work, where the windows are always being put through, and there is always an ambulance for the poor old lady who always has a fall.

He always tries to take his missus and his kids out whenever possible, always looking in the newspaper for a free day out at a nice place, heading to a museum so his little boy can run about gobsmacked at how tall the sculptures are, excited to look at statues in chain mail with his mother.

Then, on one day out, while Darren is at the toilet, he catches a tour guide talking about how much this jewel is worth. He immediately imagines how much better his family's life would be. He starts scoping out places where he could enter to steal this jewel, figuring out who he could sell it to, what tools he'd need and who could help him to steal it. But he's always had good morals; he never even stole a quid out of his mum's purse as a young boy, and he's constantly wanting to help people in need. He spends his nights counselling his friends through their problems. He's struggled himself since school, because he only got his Maths and PE GCSEs, and the bills with the distinctive red marking of 'URGENT' start to stack up, but he still makes time for others.

As the evening sets in, he puts on his boilersuit and beanie and gets ready to set off. He jumps in his 2009 white Ford Transit that was handed down to him by his mate Russell. As he starts the engine and put the directions into his phone, the regret starts setting in. His screensaver is a picture of his parents, one who died of cancer and the other who died of being heartbroken (if that's even a medical term). He starts thinking about his childhood, when he was handed to a foster home. These thoughts distract him, and he takes a wrong turn on the way to the museum. He decides to stop. Minutes later, he restarts the engine and starts the journey home, wiping a tear from his cheek.

Eight Things Not to Do in an Operating Room!

Connor Wilson

1. Make eye contact.
2. Laugh when the patient tells you they're scared.
3. Spit in the patient's mouth.
4. Tickle their ears.
5. Think about eating their insides (even if they look like sausages).
6. Say 'Ooh, moist' when you open their stomach.
7. Say 'You'll end up in stiches after we're finished' to the patient.
8. Bring a machete instead of a scalpel.

Biographies

ALICE BAZELY: I'm not quite sure what to write for my biography, but here goes…

I was born, I'm now fourteen, I love playing football, hanging out with my friends and reading. I think that pretty much sums up me.

ARLO LLOYD: I was born thirteen and a half years ago. It has gone by so quickly when you look back on it and yet so agonisingly slow when it passes before your eyes. Isn't life just a slow wait until death? Anyway, enough existential nihilism, I hope you like my illustrations.

BEN REED: I just got winded by a stair rail, so when I get home I'll probably be even more inspired to take a nap – if you couldn't guess, this is my favourite pastime. Never mind, I'll probably just watch YouTube and, yes, this is probably the worst biography you've ever read.

BRYAN NORMINTON: Hi. My hobby is gardening because it's calm and muddy, and I like writing because it lets my imagination run wild. I like writing about random stuff because I'm funny, weird and a bit quiet. I write all my emotion in a story.

DANIEL BELL: I'm a very strange boyo. I'm not the best with people, but I don't hate them all. A big boy pro-gamer I will be, with a future as hazy as an icy battlefield in a competitive Pokémon match. I'm not very funny.

ELEANOR ANNESS: Writing, reading, drawing, photography – that's all the useful information about me.

ELLIE COLLINGE: I'm a very loving person, but I am not very creative, even though I would love to be. I can be very loud when I want to be, and I like all things cute and fluffy. I think it is important to know that I hate writing about myself, but I've been asked to, so here it is.

EMILIA LOFTHOUSE: I'm open to share, and I have trouble with stories but, with help, I'm good to go.

EVA MURRAY: Mushroom hater, mess maker, fiction reader, people helper.

GALLAGHER WRIGHT: A biography I'm supposed to write. It kinda took me all night. I thought I should shout out Jeb L old sport, but that's just made me distraught. So, if you are kind, leave me alone with my brilliant mind.

GEORGE GRECH: I'm a bit short, or I used to be, I'm not sure anymore, but I like origami, I know that, and drawing… and reading… and cooking… and walking. I think that's pretty much it.

HANNAH GOULDEN: I was born in 2006 (would rather it was 1970, and then I could have been a teen in the '80s, but whatever), and I find it incredibly concerning when people say that '70s and '80s music isn't good. I love *Labyrinth* and other strange films (especially if they have David Bowie in them). I speak two languages fluently: English and swears. I live by one quote: 'Watch out where the hustlers go, and don't you eat that yellow snow.'

HARRY ARMITAGE: I like going places, I like video games, I like my TV, but most of all, I like making people happy and smile. I love helping people when they need it.

IOSAC O'MALLEY: I have a red fox Labrador. I play guitar. I like to read. I don't usually draw, and this is unusual for me.

JACK GRIFFIN: Hello, I'm a thirteen-year-old boy. I love chicken nuggets, and I hate liquorice. I play Minecraft, and I never mine at night. I'm really excited for the book to be published, and so is my mum, and that is my biography.

JOSH SHACKLETON: Loving, funny, helpful and imaginative (contributed by Milly).

LIAM EGARS: Hi, my name is Liam. I'm currently sitting here with a fractured arm and that says a lot about me because I'm pretty stupid.

LIBBY ELLIOTT: I like sports, travelling, and reading and writing.

LILY-MAE SIMPKINS: I don't know, you tell me.

MILLY STARKEY: Hardworking, funny, kind and easy to talk to (all contributed by others and not by myself).

ROMANO VIRR: Hi, I'm Romano, or you can call me Romeo as everyone else does. I love gaming 24/7 in a dark, cold room. I also have a dog called Hudson and two guinea pigs called Fudge and Spike. Keep on gaming.

ROSE BEETHAM: Short, kind, artistic and funny.

RUBY-ROSE CROSDALE: Ace, conscientious, caring and loyal (all contributed by others and not by myself).

RUBY ROBINSON: I laugh at literally anything, I like to play football and rugby, and my favourite food is pizza.

SABEER AHMED: I really like playing sports with my friends and going to competitions. I am really good at FIFA and play it in my spare time. I recently learned how to solve a Rubik's Cube and now I can't stop. Sporty, funny, friendly and mathematics – that is what you need to know about me.

SAM LINES: I love playing my guitar and dogs – especially my little Cockapoo, Willow. She never fails to put a smile on your face!

ACKNOWLEDGEMENTS

Melanie Curtis at Avon DataSet for her overwhelming support for First Story and for giving her time in typesetting this anthology.

Alison Key for proofreading this anthology.

Lee Harrison for designing the cover of this anthology.

Foysal Ali at Aquatint for printing this anthology at a discounted rate.

HRH The Duchess of Cornwall, Patron of First Story.

The Founders of First Story:
Katie Waldegrave and William Fiennes.

The Trustees of First Story:
Ed Baden-Powell (chair), Aziz Bawany, Aslan Byrne, Sophie Harrison, Sue Horner, Sarah Marshall, Bobby Nayyar, Jamie Waldegrave and Ella White.

Thanks to our funders:
Amazon Literary Partnership, the Authors' Licensing and Collecting Society (ALCS), Arts Council England, BBC Children in Need, Fiona Byrd, Beth & Michele Colocci, The Blue Thread, Didymus, the Dulverton Trust, the Garfield Weston Foundation, the Goldsmith's Company Charity, Granta Trust, Jane & Peter Aitken, John R Murray Charitable Trust, Letters Live, Man Charitable Trust, The Mayor's Young Londoners Fund, the Mercers' Company Charity, the Network for Social Change, the Paul Hamlyn Foundation, the Stonegarth Fund, Tim Bevan & Amy Gadney, the Unwin Charitable Trust, the Walcot Foundation, the Whitaker Charitable Trust, the Friends of First Story and our regular supporters, individual donors and those who choose to remain anonymous.

Pro bono supporters and delivery partners including:
Authorfy, BBC Teach, British Library, Cambridge University, Centre for Literacy in Primary Education, Driver Youth Trust, English and Media Centre, Forward Arts Foundation, Greenwich University, Hachette, National Literacy Trust, Penguin Random House and Walker Books.

Most importantly we would like to thank the students, teachers and writers who have worked so hard to make First Story a success this year, as well as the many individuals and organisations (including those who we may have omitted to name) who have given their generous time, support and advice.